Logic Puzzles For Kids Ages 8-10

This book belongs to:

_____

Thank you for choosing our logic puzzle book. It's great that you like logic puzzles as much as we do! These activities offer hours of fun and are a great way to enhance your brain functions and critical thinking skills.

There are all kind of logic puzzles in this book. We've organized it from easy to hard difficulty levels!

Once you complete the book, there will be a nice gift waiting for you as your reward.

Have fun and enjoy!

D1279463

Level 1

Let's start! In this level, you will go through easy puzzles.

Ready? Let's go!

What Comes Next?

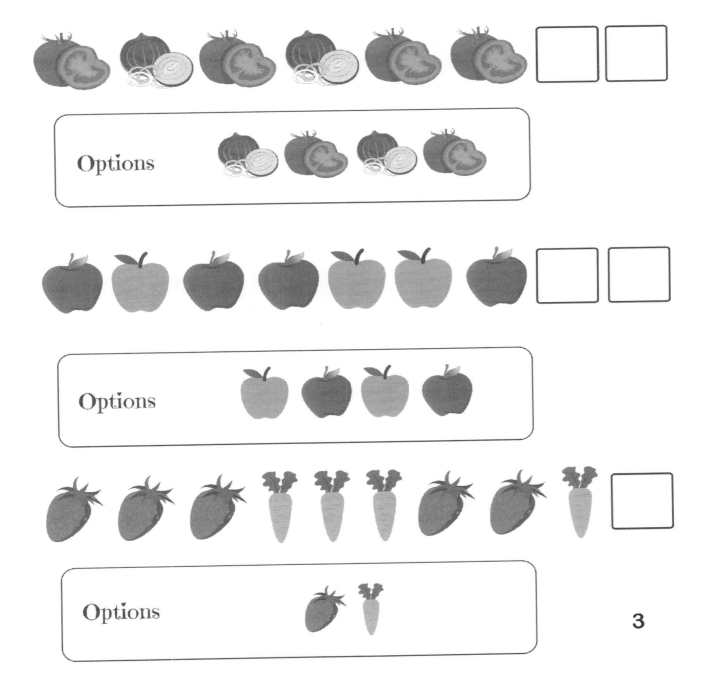

Options

Options

Options

3

What Does Not Fit?

Write your answer here:

Write your answer here:

  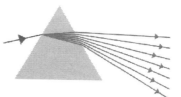 

Write your answer here:

Sudoku

What Comes Next?

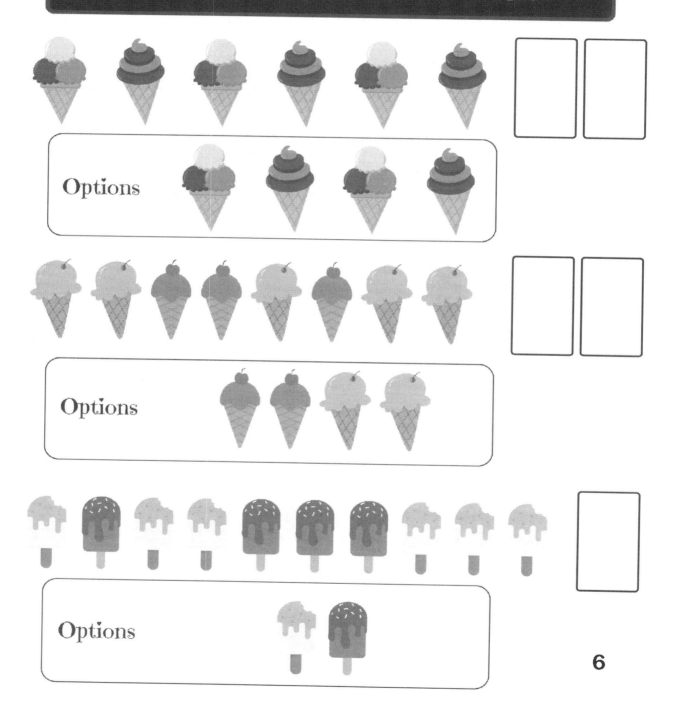

Options

Options

Options

6

What Comes Next?

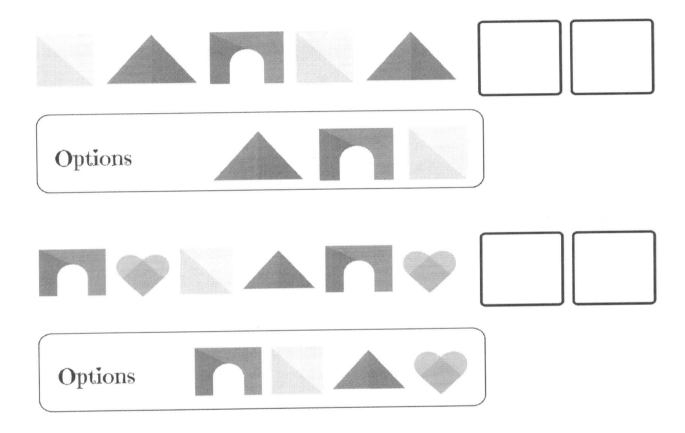

Options

Options

7

Sudoku

Find The Mistakes

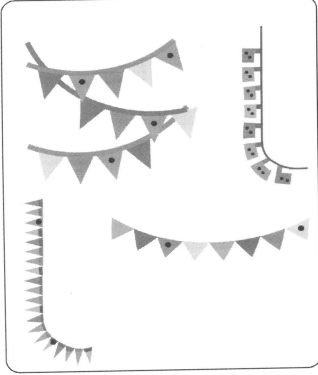

What Does Not Fit?

Write your answer here:

Write your answer here:

Write your answer here:

10

Find The Mistakes

Find The Differences

Match The Same Candies

Use different colors to match the each set of candies.

Cross Match The Same Pictures

Color and Match the Correct Part

Find Two Same Pictures

Find Two Same Pictures

Find Two Same Pictures

Match the Opposites

Level 2

In this level, you will go through medium difficulty puzzles.

Ready? Let's go!

Find Two Same Leaves

Match The Pictures

Find Two Same Flowers

Animal Pattern Matching

Pattern Belongs To

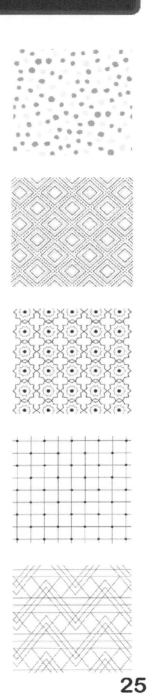

25

What Does Not Fit?

Pet Pattern Matching

Maze Fun!

Match The Correct Puzzle Shape

Autumn Vs Spring

Identify autumn and spring things by marking autumn with orange and spring with red.

Thanksgiving Hidden Pumpkin

Find the hidden pumpkin.

Thanksgiving

Tribal Pattern Matching

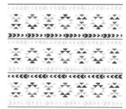

Zen doodle Find Me

Color the given picture and find a cattle and a key.

Honeycomb Sudoku

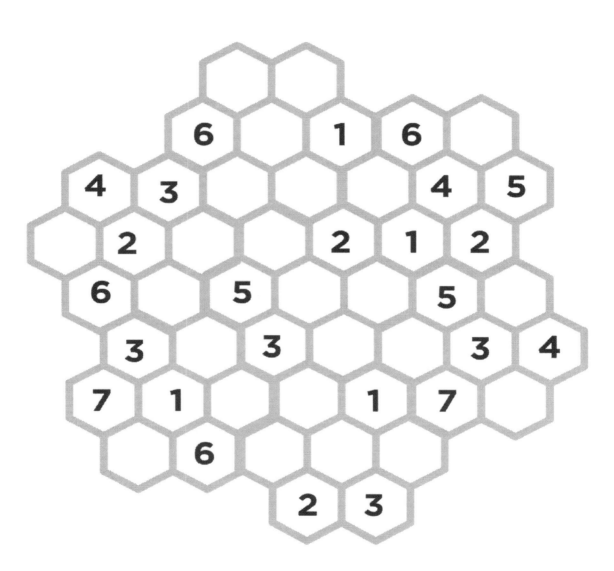

Money Math Challenge

Trace the money numbers and solve the equation.

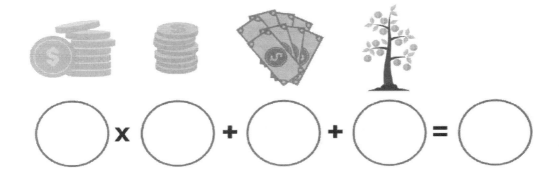

$\bigcirc \times \bigcirc + \bigcirc + \bigcirc = \bigcirc$

Math Sudoku

		9	7	3		5	2	6
		5		2		8		
6		8					4	7
					9		6	2
	4		6		3		8	
8	9		5					
2	6					1		8
		7		1		6		
9	5	1		6	4	2		

Math Labyrinth

		34	69	70	75	79
		68	62	67	72	77
12	14	34	57	62	86	82
17	19	47	52	57	92	87
22	24	42	48	53	97	99
27	32	37	41	60		
29	35	39	46	32		

Level 3

Wow you made it far!

In this level, you will go through more difficult puzzles.

Ready? Let's go!

Set The Time

Read the time from the digital clocks. Can you set the correct time on the analog clocks by drawing the correct hands?

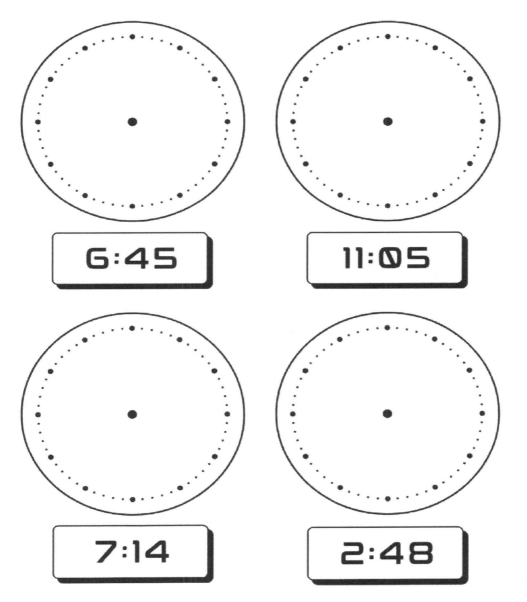

How Many?

Trace the figures and solve the equation.

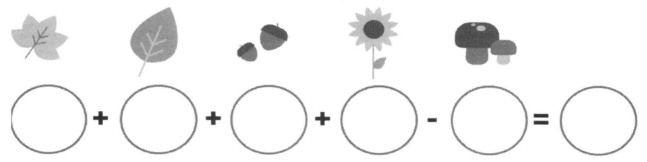

How Many?

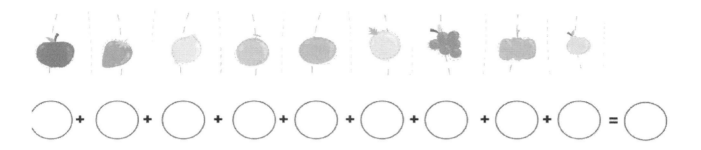

◯ + ◯ + ◯ + ◯ + ◯ + ◯ + ◯ + ◯ + ◯ = ◯

Multiplication Fun!

Solve the multiplication equations and write the correct answers in the bubbles. Then write the biggest answer in the given bubble.

13 x 12	( )	8 x 22	( )
11 x 14	( )	13 x 13	( )
5 x 28	( )	5 x -16	( )
18 x 13	( )	2 x 132	( )
-18 x -11	( )	-32 x 4	( )
14 x -8	( )	-20 x -26	( )
		?	( )

The Missing Table

8	x		=	12
12		12	=	144
13	x		=	104
91	+	79	=	
231		152	=	79
18		9	=	169
	x	17	=	85

Weight Puzzle

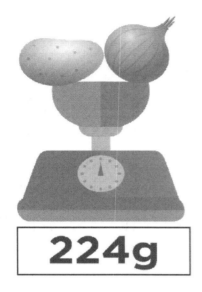

224g

245g

333g

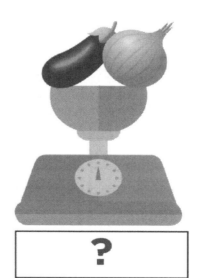

?

44

Logic Puzzle Maze Activity

Find Me

Find the only ladybug with 10 dots.

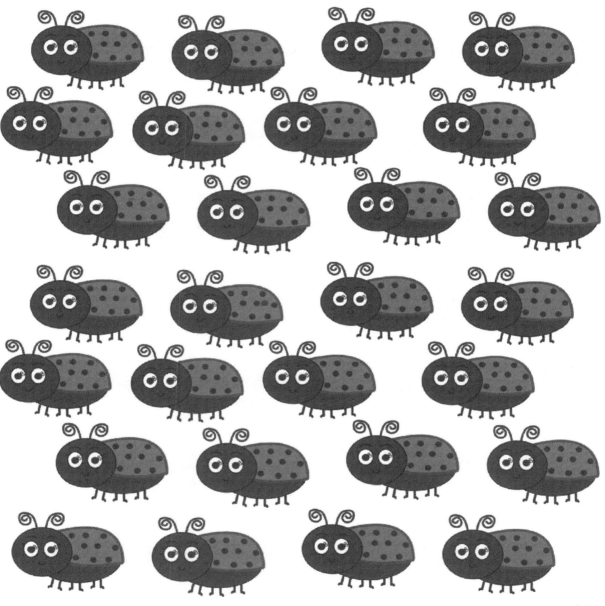

Matching Puzzle

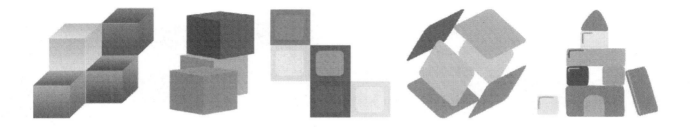

(8) (5) (6) (4) (3)

(3) (6) (4) (29) (21)

Dice Puzzle

Maze Puzzle

Tree Puzzle Activity

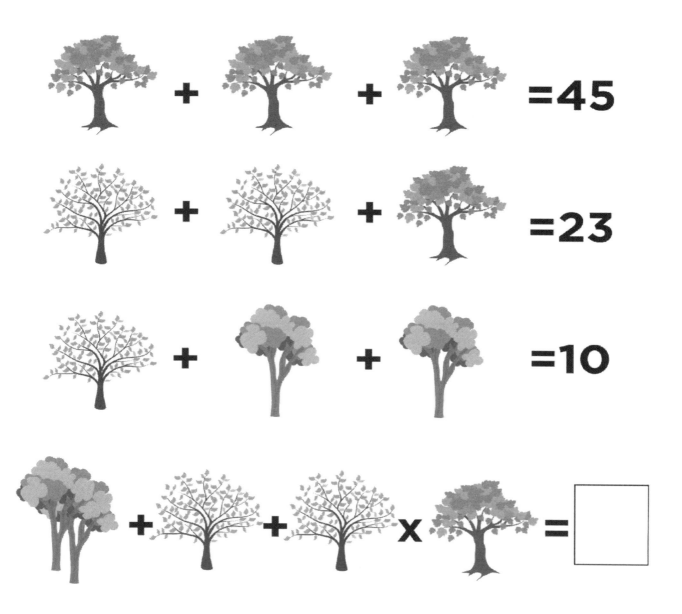

Find Me

Find the two caterpillars with missing leg.

51

Vehicle Puzzle Activity

car + car + car = 40

scooter + car + scooter = 20

scooter + motorcycle + motorcycle = 19

scooter + motorcycle × car + car = ☐

Construction Vehicle Vocabulary

Cross match the construction
vehicle to its name.

 **Truck**

 **Steamroller**

 **Crane**

 **Bulldozer**

 **Bobcat**

 **Mixer Truck**

Find Me!

Find the hidden spider.

Answer Key

Options

Options

Options

55

Answer Key

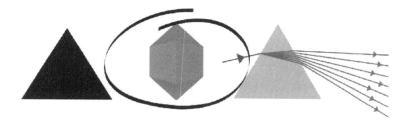

56

Answer Key

Answer Key

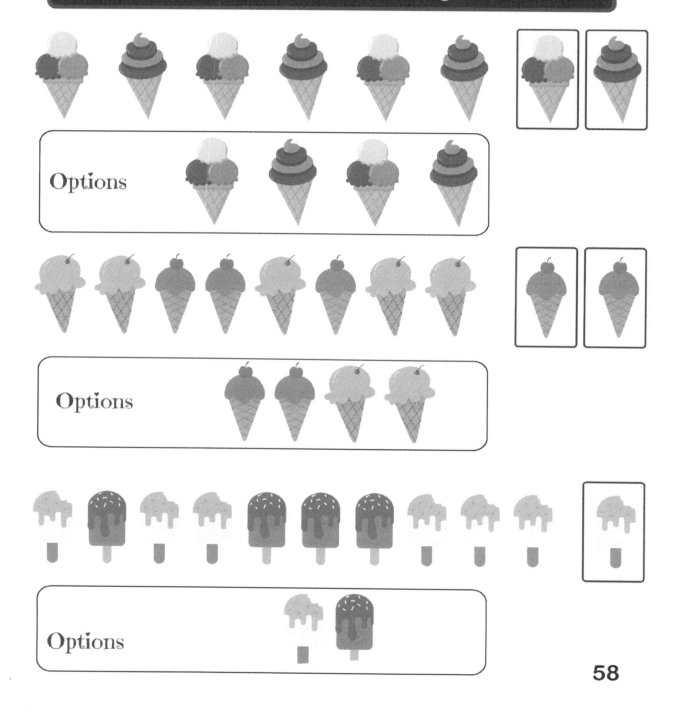

Answer Key

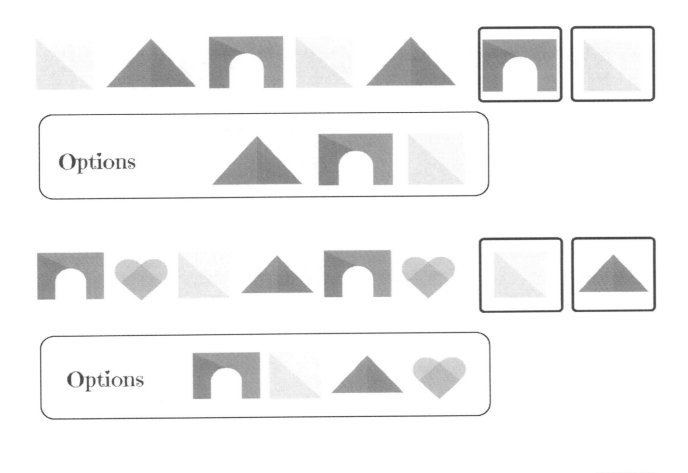

Options

Options

Answer Key

Answer Key

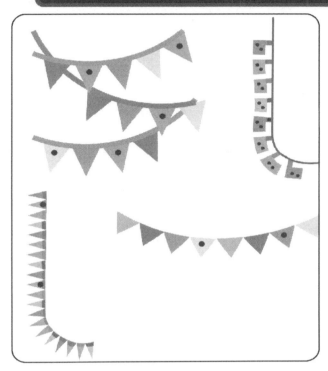

Answer Key

Write your answer here:

Write your answer here:

Write your answer here:

Answer Key

Answer Key

Answer Key

Answer Key

Answer Key

Answer Key

Answer Key

Answer Key

Answer Key

Thanksgiving

Answer Key

Answer Key

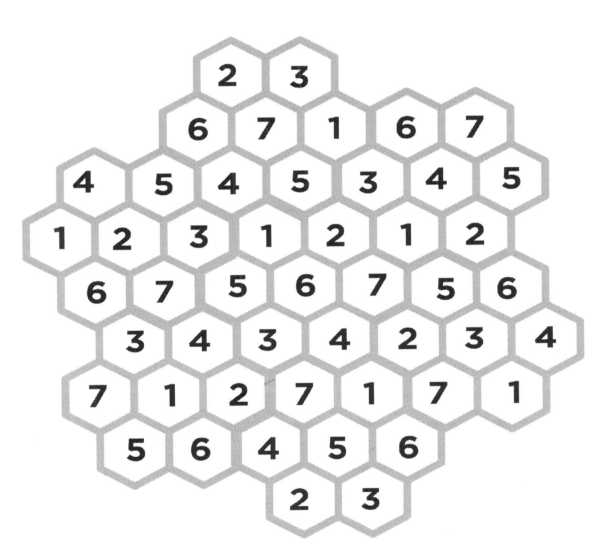

Answer Key

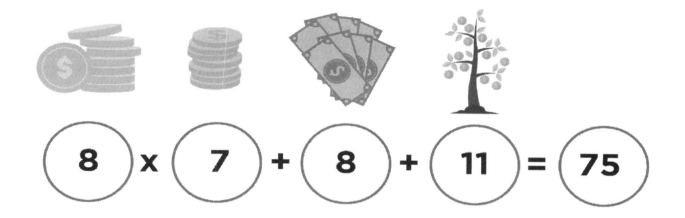

$$8 \times 7 + 8 + 11 = 75$$

1	2	9	7	3		5	2	6
3	4	5		2		8		
6	7	8					4	7
					9		6	2
	4		6		3		8	
8	9		5					
2	6					1		8
		7		1		6		
9	5	1		6	4	2		

Answer Key

		34	69	70	75	79
		68	62	67	72	77
12	14	34	57	62	86	82
17	19	47	52	57	92	87
22	24	42	48	53	97	99
27	32	37	41	60		
29	35	39	46	32		

Answer Key

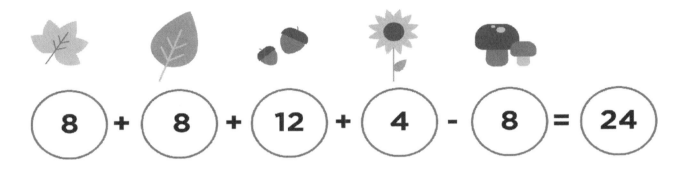

$8 + 8 + 12 + 4 - 8 = 24$

Answer Key

$8 + 8 + 6 + 6 + 6 + 6 + 7 + 5 + 8 = 54$

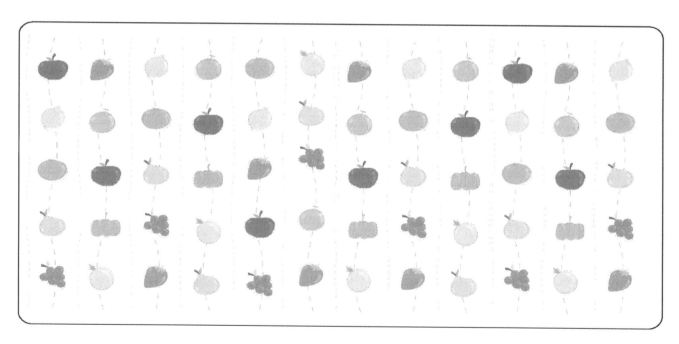

Answer Key

13 x 12	(156)	8 x 22	(176)
11 x 14	(154)	13 x 13	(169)
5 x 28	(140)	5 x -16	(-80)
18 x 13	(234)	2 x 132	(264)
-18 x -11	(198)	-32 x 4	(-128)
14 x -8	(-112)	-20 x -26	(520)

Answer (520)

Answer Key

8	x	9	=	72
12	x	12	=	144
13	x	8	=	104
91	+	79	=	176
231	-	152	=	79
18	x	9	=	169
5	x	17	=	85

Answer Key

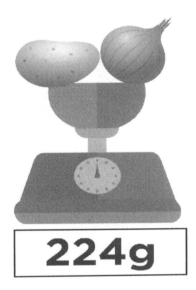

224g

245g

333g

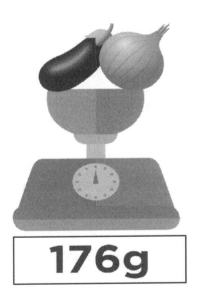

176g

Answer Key

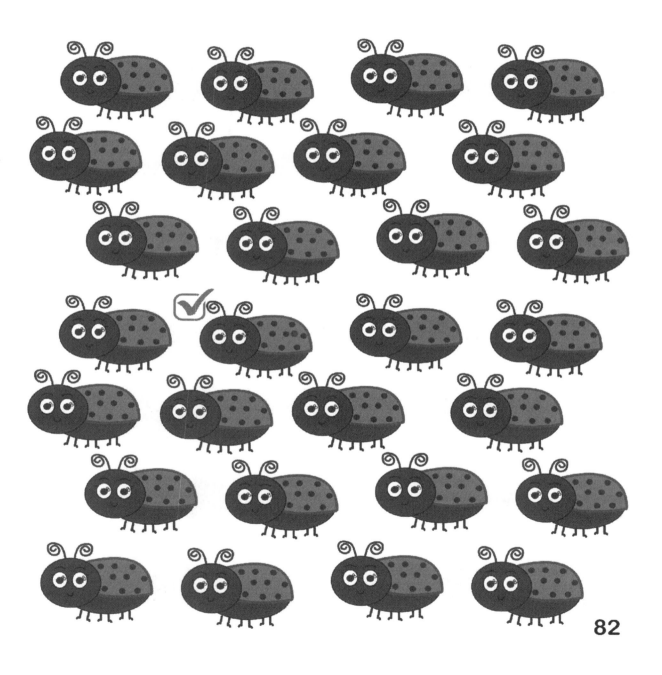

Answer Key

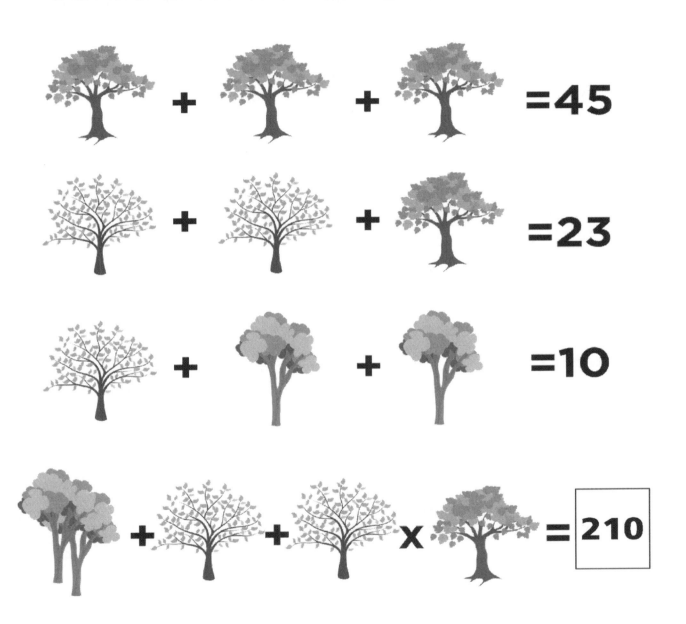

Answer Key

Answer Key

Car + Car + Car = 40

Scooter + Car + Scooter = 20

Scooter + Motorcycle + Motorcycle = 19

Scooter + Motorcycle × Car = **220**

Answer Key

CONGRATULATIONS!

Excellent work! I am sure that there were some obstacles along the way, but you persisted and finished the activities! Hooray!

I also want to give a HUGE THANKS to our staff at Kids Castle Press for making these books a reality. It wouldn't have been possible without them. Feel free to visit our website below to show them some love!

In addition, if you'd like us to send you more free content to print out, you can do so by visiting our website: www.kidscastlepress.com

To add a cherry on top... You can email us for a chance to win a free physical copy of our next book: info@kidscastlepress.com
Don't miss out as we won't be doing this forever... it's a limited time only!

Lastly, if you like this book, would you be so kind as to drop me a review on Amazon?

Thank you very much!

Jennifer L. Trace

- -

Congratulations
Logic Puzzle Star:

THE BEST!

_____

Date:_____   **Signed:**_____

Made in the USA
Las Vegas, NV
05 October 2021